I SPEND HALF MY TIME WAITING FOR SOMETHING TO HAPPEN AND THE OTHER HALF WISHING IT HADN'T

3-29

RACKING HIS BRAINS TO DREAM UP SOME GOOD NEW FIBS, WHEN I'D RATHER LISTEN TO THE SAME OLD BAD ONES AND JUST GET TO BED

WHEN YOU CAN'T *CHANGE* A BLOKE, *MANAGE* HIM, EH?

© 1992 M G N
DIST. BY SYNDICATION INTERNATIONAL NORTH
AMERICA SYNDICATE INC.

ALL RIGHT! IF YOU WANT TO SPLIT HAIRS — I SAW RUBE *COMING* INTO THE ROSE AND CROWN!!

5-10

Smith

BY THE TIME YOU'VE DECIDED TO THROW YOUR WEIGHT ABOUT, YOU FIND IT TAKES ALL YOUR TIME TO *CARRY* IT!

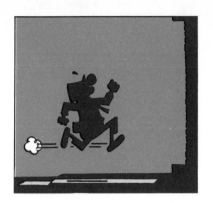

I SPEND HALF MY TIME WAITING FOR SOMETHING TO HAPPEN AND THE OTHER HALF WISHING IT HADN'T

3-29

RACKING HIS BRAINS TO DREAM UP SOME GOOD NEW FIBS, WHEN I'D RATHER LISTEN TO THE SAME OLD BAD ONES AND JUST GET TO BED

4-26

WHEN YOU CAN'T *CHANGE* A BLOKE, *MANAGE* HIM, EH?

ALL RIGHT! IF YOU WANT TO SPLIT HAIRS — I SAW RUBE *COMING* INTO THE ROSE AND CROWN!!

5-10

Smythe

BY THE TIME YOU'VE DECIDED TO THROW YOUR WEIGHT ABOUT, YOU FIND IT TAKES ALL YOUR TIME TO *CARRY* IT!

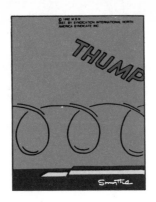

AW, DON'T BE LIKE THAT, PET. IT'S ONLY FOR THE WEEKEND

THAT WOMAN CAN STAY LONGER IN TWO DAYS THAN MOST PEOPLE CAN STAY IN TWO WEEKS !

IT REALLY UPSETS HER —THAT DEEP, UNTROUBLED SLEEP THAT ONLY SEEMS TO COME TO THOSE WHO'VE DONE NOTHING TO DESERVE IT

6-28

THAT MAN'S MIND —

7-19

MIND YOU, THERE'S SOMETHING IN WHAT HE SAYS

TELL ME ABOUT HER, JACK

SHE'S VERY BRAINY. THEY SAY SHE'S THE THINKING MAN'S TYPE OF LASS —

AND THAT'S THE SORT SHE REALLY LIKES

LOVELY. *I'M* A THINKING MAN

NOTHING COULD BE *THAT* FUNNY— HEH! HEH—!

ENJOYING Y'SELF?

Smythe 9-6

9-13

HOW ABOUT INVITING MUM TO COME WITH US?

© 1982 M.G.N.
DIST. BY PRODUCTION INTERNATIONAL NORTH
AMERICA SYNDICATE INC.

TCH! DON'T START THAT AGAIN

WEL-LL, PET, SHE GETS SICK OF HER OWN COMPANY NIGHT AFTER NIGHT

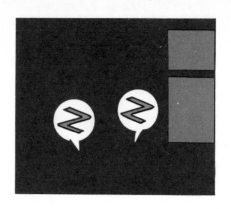

10-11

NO MEMORY IS EVER SHORT ENOUGH TO FORGET *THAT* LAD

SLAP

11-15

I COULDN'T COME, MAUREEN. I WAS PLAYING IN AN AWAY SNOOKER MATCH —

LIKE I SAID — THANKS FOR MAKING IT SUCH A LOVELY EVENING

JUST ONCE I'D LIKE US TO
DISCUSS SOMETHING WITHOUT
DRAGGING IN ARITHMETIC —!!

ALSO IN THIS SERIES

ON CUE
AFTER A FEW
DON'T WAIT UP

£2.99

Available at your local bookshop or newsagent, or can be ordered direct from the publisher. Just fill in the form below. Price and availability subject to change without notice.

Ravette Books Limited, PO Box 11, Falmouth, Cornwall, TR10 9EN

Please send a cheque or postal order for the value of the book, and add the following for postage and packing:
UK including BFPO — £1.00 per order.
OVERSEAS, including EIRE — £2.00 per order.
OR Please debit this amount from my Access/Visa Card (delete as appropriate).

Card Number: [ ][ ][ ][ ][ ][ ][ ][ ][ ][ ][ ][ ][ ][ ][ ][ ][ ][ ][ ]

EXPIRY DATE . . . .

SIGNED . . . .

NAME . . . .

ADDRESS . . . .

. . . .